Country Gardens

Merry walking tempo

English Folk Dance

Parade of the Tin Soldiers

Arranged by Denes Agay

Leon Jessel

Graceful marching tempo

Mill in the Forest

Richard Eilenberg

D.C. al Fine

Little Hungarian Rhapsody

Denes Agay

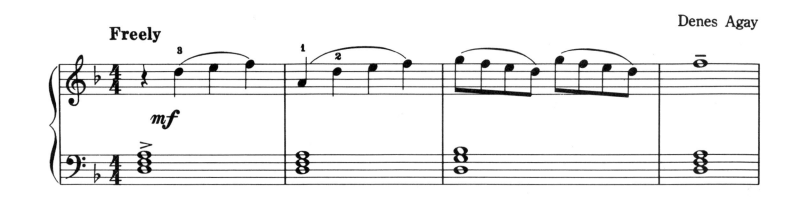

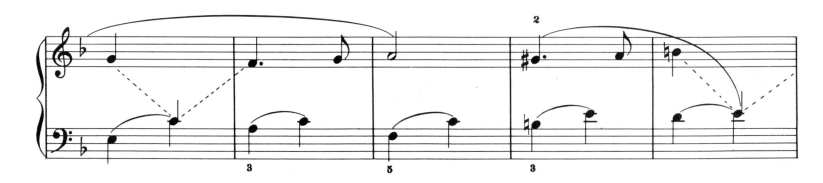

Glowworm Variations

Paul Lincke - Denes Agay

Variations on an Austrian Folk Song

Friedrich Kuhlau

Var. 3

Var. 4

Carillon on a French Carol

Moderately lively

Denes Agay

46

Lullaby

Michael Iordansky

Gently moving

The Marionette's Funeral March

Arranged by Denes Agay

Charles Gounod

The "Saints" Boogie

Lively, with a solid beat

Denes Agay

50

Recital Samba

Gerald Martin

Valse Impromptue

Allegretto ; con grazia

Fritz Spindler

Scherzo

Allegretto

Theodore Kirchner

Peasant Dance

Oskar Bolck

Prelude for Lili

Op. 119, No. 6

Stephen Heller

The Bagpipe

from "For Children" Book 2

Slowly and heavily

Béla Bartók

Riding The Hobby Horse

Op. 98, No. 5

Alexander Gretchaninoff

He galloped too far

All's well that ends well

Tarantella

Theodore Lack

The Ragtimers

Secondo

Abe Holzman

64

D.S. al Fine

The Ragtimers

Primo

Abe Holzman

65

D.S. al Fine

Strolling at Loch Lomond

Secondo

Gerald Martin

Strolling at Loch Lomond

Primo

Gerald Martin

March
from "The Love of Three Oranges"

Edited by Denes Agay

Serge Prokofieff

Vigorous march tempo

La Campanella

Transcribed by Denes Agay

Niccolo Paganini · Franz Liszt

Serenade

Stephen Heller

Festival Rondo

Henry Purcell

poco rit.

D.C. al Fine

Witches' Dance

Szidor Bátor

Murmuring Brook

Ede Poldini